dramascript

The Doctor and The Devils

by

DYLAN THOMAS

from the story by DONALD TAYLOR;

adapted for the stage by GUY WILLIAMS

MACMILLAN

First published 1969

This volume is published by arrangement with J. M. Dent
& Sons Ltd., Donald Taylor and the Trustees of the
Dylan Thomas Estate.

A fee of one guinea is payable on any public performance
of this play other than the first night of a school
performance.

First edition 1969
Reprinted 1970, 1971, 1973, 1974

Published by
MACMILLAN EDUCATION LIMITED
Basingstoke and London

Companies and representatives throughout the world

PRINTED IN HONG KONG

FOREWORD

Drama is one of the most exciting of all forms of human activity. At its best, it involves us completely—whether we are acting ourselves or watching others act—and those occasions when we are gripped by some dramatic tension may be among the most memorable moments in our lives. In this new series we hope to encourage this sort of experience.

DRAMASCRIPTS are intended for use in secondary schools, amateur theatrical groups and youth clubs. The plays range widely from established classics to new works and adaptations of books and film scripts. There is nothing in any of the plays that is beyond the capabilities of younger actors. They may be used in a variety of ways: read privately for pleasure or aloud in groups, acted in the classroom, church hall or youth club, or in public performances. The maximum enjoyment is obviously to be found in actual performance—and the benefits of acting need no elaboration—but we have borne in mind that the play must interest and entertain however it is used, and we are confident that even the solitary reader will find here something of the excitement of the live theatre.

GUY WILLIAMS
Advisory Editor

THE CHARACTERS

LUDOVICI, a boy who sells white mice
DOCTOR KNOX, a great anatomist
JAMIE, a simpleton
DAVID PATERSON, porter and doorkeeper at Doctor Knox's Anatomy
    Rooms
ALEXANDER MILLER, the Doctor's principal assistant
ANDREW MERRYLEES, ⎫
PRAYING HOWARD,   ⎬ Three Resurrectionists
THE MOLE,   ⎭
WILLIAM BURKE, an Irish labourer
WILLIAM HARE, another Irishman
AN OLD WOMAN of the Market-place
HELEN M'DOUGAL, who lives with Burke
MRS. HARE, wife of Hare
A PARISH CARPENTER
FIRST STUDENT of the Anatomy Classes
SECOND STUDENT
A HAWKER
OLD JOSEPH, an ailing guest at Log's Lodging House
A SMALL SAVAGE BOY
A LITTLE OLD WOMAN, found in the gutter
A BEGGAR MAN
GRAY, a middle-aged lodger
MRS. GRAY, his wife
THE GRAYS' BABY, can be a doll or dummy
A GROCER
MRS. DOCHERTY, an old woman from Donegal
BURKE'S BROTHER
A POLICEMAN
A LITTLE GIRL

Citizens, more students, more policemen, children.

In the script prepared by Dylan Thomas, the names of the characters were changed, to conform with film censorship. In this version, the original names have been restored.

The action takes place in a City Market Place, an Anatomy Theatre, and Log's Lodging House.

PRACTICAL ANATOMY
and
OPERATIVE SURGERY

DR. KNOX'S rooms for practical anatomy and operative surgery, will open on Monday, the 6th of October, and continue open until the End of July 1829.

Two DEMONSTRATIONS will be delivered daily to the Gentlemen attending the Rooms for PRACTICAL ANATOMY. These Demonstrations will be arranged so as to comprise complete Courses of the DESCRIPTIVE ANATOMY of the Human Body, with its application to PATHOLOGY and OPERATIVE SURGERY. The Dissections and Operations to be under the immediate superintendence of DR. KNOX. Arrangements have been made to secure as usual an ample supply of Anatomical Subjects.

FEE for the First Course, £3,5s.; Second Course, £2,4s.; Perpetual, £5,9s.

N.B.–An Additional Fee of Three Guineas includes Subjects.

∵ Certificates of Attendance on these Courses qualify for Examination before the Royal Colleges of Surgeons, the Army and Navy Medical Boards, &c.

EDINBURGH, 10 SURGEONS' SQUARE
25th September 1828

–Bill Advertising Doctor Knox's Lectures, 1828

The Scene: An early nineteenth-century City—a compact wilderness of little archwayed courts and closes, sunless dead ends, market spaces surrounded by tumbling top-heavy tenements, hovels, cottages and pigsties . . .

The whole, or the largest part, of the acting area may well represent the City Market Place. Within this, or adjoining it, there should be two distinct zones at different levels—the lower zone, to represent the living room of a common lodging house, referred to as 'Log's'; the higher, to represent a lecture platform at Doctor Knox's Rooms for Practical Anatomy and Operative Surgery. If possible, a doorway should be provided near the lower zone to suggest that there is an inner, hidden room at the lodging house. A stout table or demonstration bench is all that is needed to furnish the Anatomy Theatre, though other features may be added at the discretion of the producer.

Changes of scene can be readily indicated by changes of lighting, or by concentrating the attention of the audience on one particular part of the acting area.

I
A CITY MARKET PLACE

(Up come the City sounds, suggesting that:
The straw-strewn cobbles of the market are crowded with stalls. Stalls that sell rags and bones, kept by rags and bones. Stalls that sell odds and ends of every odd kind, odd boots, bits of old meat, fish heads, trinkets, hats with feathers, broadsheets, hammers. Stalls with shawls. Stalls like ash bins. Anything that is marketable, to the very poor.

Pigs and chickens grunt, root, cluck and peck among the straw heaps and the refuse, getting in everyone's way though

1

no one notices or cares.

The doors of the shops and the public-houses are open on to the Market, and singing comes from inside some of them, and outside some of them stand men and women drinking and singing.

There are many, many children, some very old.

One child, the gentle **Ludovici,** *has a little wheel cage that contains white mice. He takes one of the mice out of the cage and plays with it for a moment, until a man in a cloak and top-hat walks across the market towards him.)*

Ludovici. Will ye buy my tame mice? Will ye buy my tame mice? They don't cost much. They don't eat much. Will ye buy my tame mice? . . .

(To the man in the cloak and top-hat, who is **Doctor Knox.***)*

. . . Would ye like one of my tame mice, Sir? Or two, so that they can be company? One mouse all by itself is sure to be lonely.

Doctor Knox. Tame mice, boy? No. Why should I want a tame mouse?

Ludovici. If I can't sell my white mice, Sir, I'll have to go to the Poorhouse. It's a terrible place, the Poorhouse. Ye can have any one of them, Sir, any one you fancy, except wee Maria over there. I'm not parting wi' her.

Doctor Knox *(Leaning over the cage).* Which is wee Maria?

Ludovici. The one wi' a black spatchie near her left eye, Sir. I wouldna part wi' her for anything.

Doctor Knox. Is she a friend of yours?

Ludovici. She is that, Sir. She's the only one of my mice that lived wi' me through the last terrible winter. We had nothing to keep warm with, and not very much to eat, ever. When ye've been through a winter like that wi' a mouse, Sir, ye wouldna part wi' her for a whole gold sovereign. And the children she has! Ye wouldna believe a wee mouse could have so many children, Sir. . . But. . . Would ye no like one of the other mice?

Doctor Knox. What is your name, my child?

Ludovici. They call me Ludovici, Sir. Ludovici of the mice.

Doctor Knox. That is not a Scottish name—Ludovici?

Ludovici. I know it, Sir. My father and my mother came from Italy, but they are both deid, and now I am all alone. Will ye no buy one of my mice?

Doctor Knox. I'll not buy one of your mice, Ludovici, but here . . .

*(*Doctor Knox *puts money gently into* Ludovici's *hand.)*

. . . is a small present for you. Take it and buy yourself something good to eat with it.

Ludovici. It's a crown piece! It's a crown piece! Oh, thank ye, Sir! Maria, we're in luck! Ye can have milk wi' your bread, the night! We can both have milk wi' our bread, the night! Oh, thank ye, Sir! Thank ye!

(As Doctor Knox *walks away from the market place we hear the cry of a woman selling rags and hucksters' scraps.)*

First Market Woman *(Known, later, as* Helen M'Dougal*)*. Rags and bones . . . Rags and bones . . .

Second Market Woman *(Known, later, as* Mrs. Hare*)*. Cat-skin . . . Human hair . . .

First Market Woman. Rags, rags . . . Rags and bones . . .

Second Market Woman. Cat-skin . . . Human hair . . .

(A Rude Bystander *mimics their cries. Then* James Wilson, *known usually as* 'Daft'Jamie, *comes across to* Ludovici. *He is a simple but harmless youth—ragged, bare headed, and unshod.)*

Jamie. What did he give you, Ludovici? What did the Doctor give you?

Ludovici. He didna give me anything, Jamie . . . Leastways, nothing that he'd want me to tell you about.

Jamie. Gie us some then, Ludovici. Gie us some of what he gived you. Come on.

Ludovici. What's the use of giving you anything, Jamie? Ye'd only lose it. Or you'd put it in a hole in the ground and then you'd forget where you'd hidden it. You know you're not very bright upstairs.

Jamie. I wouldna . . .

*(Jamie *is getting worked up like a spoiled child that cannot get its own way.)*

. . . I wouldna. I wouldna. I wouldna.

Ludovici. You would. Look at the hat and the shoes the Doctor gave you afore. You haven't put them on yet, have you? Not once? . . .

*(Jamie *shakes his head dumbly.)*

. . . Why not? Why haven't you put them on?

Jamie. Because I dinna want to wear them in sic hard times as these.

Ludovici. That's no good reason.

Jamie. It is. What'll I do for more, when they're worn out?

Ludovici. Oh, Jamie, you're hopeless. Look. If I do give you any money, all to yourself, you'll only go and spend it on snuff, or something that won't do you a bit of good.

Jamie. I like snuff. What for shouldn't I like snuff, Ludovici?

Ludovici. I tell you what, Jamie. We're going to have a wee bit bigger supper tonight, the mice and I, with what the Doctor has given us. You come along with me now. If you're good, and quiet, we'll gie you a share, too. Would you like that? . . .

(Daft Jamie nods, with enthusiasm.)

. . . Come on, then.

(The two boys leave the Market Place. As they go, we hear the voices of the two Market Women.)

First Market Woman. Rags, rags . . . Rags and bones . . .

Second Market Woman. Cat-skin . . . Human hair . . .

2

THE ANATOMY THEATRE

(As Doctor Knox approaches the platform of his Anatomy Theatre, ready to lecture to his students, David Paterson, the Porter and Doorkeeper at the Anatomy Rooms, speaks to him.)

David Paterson. They're here, Doctor Knox.

(Doctor Knox stops.)

Doctor Knox. Indeed, Mr. Paterson? Who or what are 'they', and where is 'here'?

David Paterson. The specimens for the Anatomical Museum, Sir, are in the Museum.

Doctor Knox. How fortunate they are not in the gentlemen's cloak room . . . Thank you . . .

(He hands his hat and cloak to David Paterson and we see that he is wearing a long, dark coat, immaculately tailored, and an ornate

4

embroidered waistcoat across which gold chains hang in festoons.
As the **Students** *assemble, he seems to be preening himself; he*
flicks off invisible dust. The arrival of **Alexander Miller,** *the*
Doctor's *principal assistant, is the signal for the lecture to begin.)*

. . . I stand before you, gentlemen, as a lecturer in Anatomy, a
scientist, a specialist, a *material* man to whom the heart, for
instance, is an elaborate physical organ and not the 'seat of love',
a man to whom the 'soul', because it has no shape, does not
exist.

But paradox is inherent in all dogma, and so I stand before
you also as a man of sentiment, of spiritual aspirations, intellectually
creative impulses, social convictions, moral passions. And it is in
my dual capacity of scientist and sociologist, materialist and
moralist, anatomist and artist, that I shall attempt to conduct my
lectures, to expound, inform, illustrate, entertain, and edify . . .

*(*Doctor Knox, *as a lecturer, shows a rare felicity of movement,*
now reminding us of the slow and graceful minuet, then the quiet
pose of soldierly attention; and these again are succeeded by the
rapid gesture.)

. . . Our aim for ever must be the pursuit of the knowledge of
Man in his entirety. To study the flesh, the skin, the bones, the
organs, the nerves of Man, is to equip our minds with a knowledge
that will enable us to search *beyond* the body. The noble
profession at whose threshold you stand as neophytes is not an
end in itself. The science of Anatomy contributes to the great
sum of all Knowledge, which is the Truth: the whole Truth of
the Life of Man upon this turning earth. And so, observe
precisely. Record exactly. Neglect nothing. Fear no foe. Never
swerve from your purpose. Pay no heed to Safety.

For I believe that all men can be happy, and that the good
life can be led upon this earth.

I believe that all men must work towards that end.

And I believe that that end justifies any means . . .
Let no scruples stand in the way of the progress of medical
science!
Gentlemen, you may continue your researches . . .

*(*Doctor Knox *bows: a curt but studied bow. The students return*
his bow. Alexander Miller *makes a gesture of dismissal to the*
students, who disperse. The students suddenly begin talking, as

they move away. **Doctor Knox** *nods towards the noise.)*

. . . What do they talk about afterwards, I wonder? Do they repeat one's words of golden guidance? Or make disparaging remarks about one's waistcoat? I think when I was a student we used to tell one another stories: they were anatomical, too . . . Ah, thank you, Paterson.

*(***Doctor Knox** *takes his hat and cape from the Porter, then he gives him a curt nod of dismissal.)*

Alexander Miller. You agree with all you said?

Doctor Knox. But naturally.

Alexander Miller. 'The end justifies *any* means'? This is—to say the least of it—unscrupulous.

Doctor Knox. Then do not say 'the least of it'. Say 'the most': that it is *honest* . . .

*(***Alexander Miller** *gives a little shrug.)*

. . . You're coming to my dinner, of course?

Alexander Miller. Of course.

Doctor Knox. I can guarantee the cooking. Only the conversation will be half-baked, and only the politeness overdone.

Alexander Miller *(With a kind of tolerant affection).* Dinner will be a monologue, as usual, Robert. I can't think how you ever manage to eat or drink anything at all on these occasions.

Doctor Knox. I eat during the yawns . . .

*(***Alexander Miller** *helps him on with his cloak.)*

. . . I *loathe* all Dinners with a capital 'D'. Why can't I have a *quiet* meal with a small 'm' and a large port?

Alexander Miller. Oh, but Robert! A Dinner to Celebrate the Opening of the New Session of Doctor Knox's Academy . . .

Doctor Knox. I wish it were still Barclay's and Knox's Academy . . .

(He speaks as though to himself.)

. . . Poor Barclay. He was as stern as a judge and as solid as a mountain. When I was a student, he had the bearing and the voice of a god surrounded by the angels of logic. He founded this school to keep the teaching of Anatomy away from hacks and drudges and medical impostors, crammers, and quacks . . .

6

from men like Munro, for instance, who reads his grandfather's lectures for his own, and dissects like a labourer with a pick . . .

(He puts on his top-hat and speaks suddenly in a different mood.)

. . . If my sister hasn't invited at least one mentally deficient Duke I shall be so surprised that I shall have to ask one myself. And throw in a drunk baronet for bad measure. Good night, Miller.

Alexander Miller. Good night. Sleep well.

Doctor Knox. Don't be a dam' fool . . . How can a man with a busy brain like mine sleep?

*(**Alexander Miller** smiles after him as they go their separate ways.)*

3

THE MARKET PLACE

*(A crowd of **Savages**, small ragged urchins, appear.)*

The Savages. Where's Ludovici? . . .

*(They see **Ludovici**.)*

. . . There's Ludovici! Come here, Ludovici, we've got a present for you! Give it to him, Sandy.

*(One **Savage** holds up a box tied with string.)*

Ludovici. What for do you want to give me a present?

The Savages. Because we like you, Ludovici. Because we like you. Because we like you. Because we like you.

Ludovici *(Looking at the box).* It's the first time ye've liked me enough to give me a present. What's in it?

The Savages. It's a surprise, Ludovici. It's a surprise. It's a surprise. It's a surprise.

Ludovici. I don't want it, thank you very much.

First Savage. Go on, Ludovici. Open it. See what it is.

The Savages. See what it is. See what it is. See what it is.

Ludovici. No, thank you. I wasna born yesterday. Ye know where ye can throw your present.

First Savage. Ach, Ludovici's too sly for us. Let's give it to Jamie. Come here, Jamie . . .

7

(Jamie approaches.)

. . . We've got a present for you. Give it to him, Sandy.

Jamie. What for do you want to gi'e me a present?

The Savages. Because we like you, Jamie. Because we like you. Because we like you.

Jamie. What's in it?

The Savages. Open it, Jamie. Open it and see.

Jamie. Is it . . . food?

The Savages. It might be food, Jamie. Pasties and pies and pancakes and neeps. Yes, it might be food.

Jamie. Is it . . . Is it something to keep me warm at night?

The Savages. It might be something to keep you warm at night, Jamie.

First Savage. A blanket, maybe. With Jamie's own tartan. But why not open it now and see?

Jamie. How'll I open it?

The Savages. Ye'll have to untie the knots, Jamie.

Jamie. Untie the knots?

First Savage. Aye. Or cut the string. Here. Here's a wee knife to cut the string . . . There!

Jamie *(Unwrapping).* It might be food . . . It might be something to keep me warm . . . It might be . . .

(He gets the parcel open at last.)

. . . It's a . . .

(He pulls out a skull. **The Savages** *scream with laughter.)*

(It is night, and the market place is crowded—some of those present are singing, as though they have been over-enjoying themselves in the neighbouring taverns. Three men are definitely drunk, though solemnly so, as befits men whose business is death. The three **Drunken Men** *raise their tankards to each other.)*

First Drunken Man. To the dead!

Second Drunken Man. To the Surgeons of our City!

(They drink. Now we see, quite close to them, **William Burke** *and* **William Hare,** *two men of the market place. They are listening hard, but cautiously, to the other three.)*

8

Third Drunken Man. It's been a good month. I'm thirsty.

Second Drunken Man. A blessed month.

First Drunken Man. Subjects like penny pies. Plenty of 'em. I'm thirsty too, Mole. I've drunk three pints o' gin. And I'm goin' to drink *three pints more* . . .

Second Drunken Man. Careful, careful, Andrew, you'll get the taste for it.

> *(The three of them croak and laugh, without smiling, like three carrion crows.*
> *And* **Burke** *and* **Hare** *are listening all the time.*
> **Burke** *beckons, secretly, with a stubby black finger, to an old woman, all rags and bones, standing near them.)*

Burke *(In a rough, Irish whisper).* Who would they be with all that money for the drink?

The Old Woman *(Whispering back).* Andrew Merry-Lees, and Praying Howard, and . . . and . . . the Mole.

Burke. And what do they do for a living, my lovey?

The Old Woman *(A sharp whisper, full of fear).* Body-snatchers.

> *(***Burke*** *makes a movement as though to cross himself, then lets his hand fall, and looks at his companion.)*

Hare *(Through thin, side-twisted lips).* Body-snatchers . . .

The Old Woman. Aye. Fourteen pounds for a corpse they get when its digged up new. Fourteen pounds. From the surgeons.

Burke. Fourteen pounds?

The Old Woman. Aye, so they say. They're always around, when a body is dying, one or other of them. I mind an auld friend of mine, who was in a poorly way. 'When wull we come for the corp'?' she heard one of them say. She got out of her bed quickly enough after that, and can you blame her?

> *(Shouts and laughter, and a wet dribble of singing come from the shadows that are packed tight with beggars, hawkers, cheapjacks, drunks, rogues and slummers.* **Burke** *and* **Hare** *move across to the two* **Market Women** *we noticed in the first scene.)*

Burke *(Ingratiatingly, yet with an under-menace to one of them).* Can you buy a little drink for us, Nelly me darling? We're thirsty, love.

Hare *(To the second* **Market Woman**, *who is his wife).* Can you buy a little drink for Burke and Hare, Burke and Hare . . .

Helen M'Dougal. There's money for two more and that's all. Here, buy 'em yourself, William Burke.

*(She tosses **Burke** a coin. As he catches it and shoulders his way off to the bar, **Hare** reaches for **Helen M'Dougal's** drink. The woman makes as if to snatch the tankard back, but **Hare** suddenly shows his teeth and pretends to snap at her.)*

Mrs. Hare. Ach, leave him be. Hare's got the devil in him tonight. He'd bite your hand through, if you let him get near enough to you. I know him.

*(**Burke** returns with two drinks. He hands one to **Hare**, who attacks it hungrily. Then **Burke** sees the three **Drunken Men** move off into the shadows.)*

Burke *(To the women).* Them three is body snatchers, see 'em? They're off on their round, I'll lay . . .

(His voice lowers.)

. . . They've always got plenty to drink . . I'll wager they've gone to dig up another, tonight. It's dark enough for them, there's not a big moon . . .

*(He turns to look at **Hare**, who is staring after the body-snatchers with glinting eyes.)*

. . . Fourteen pounds for a corpse they get, she said, when it's digged up new. Fourteen pounds!

Hare. Fourteen pounds for gin and pies . . .

Mrs. Hare. Hush! You mad dog . . . We've got the lodging house. What more d'you want?

Helen M'Dougal. There's no more left.

Burke. Come on, Nelly darlin', scrape up a penny or two for a drop for us . . . There's plenty of ways, lovey . . .

*(**Helen M'Dougal** walks to a barrow heaped with rags and takes the handles.)*

Helen M'Dougal. There's no more, I say.

*(With a yelp, **Hare** leaps on to the barrow, sitting bolt upright among the rags.)*

Hare *(In a high, gay snarl).* Hare In his carriage and pair . . .

(Helen M'Dougal *takes no notice but starts to push the barrow away.*)

Burke. Fourteen pounds for a corpse!

Helen M'Dougal (*In a harsh grumble as she trundles the barrow on with its load of rags and one cackling man*). Why don't you dig one up yourself? You're frightened of the dark . . .

(Hare *points his finger at one dark doorway, then at another.*)

Hare. They're dead in there . . . Dig 'em up, Burke . . . In there . . . In there . . .

(*The barrow, with its motley escort, rattles off to Rag-and-Bone Alley.*)

4
THE ANATOMY THEATRE

(Doctor Knox *enters, and the* Students *assemble. The* Doctor *is like a great actor; he acknowledges the ovation of his audience; he bows; he steps to the platform table; he adjusts his spectacles and his cuffs; every movement is studied.*)

Doctor Knox. Gentlemen . . .

(*He has a large volume in his hand.*)

. . . This, gentlemen, is a volume by Vesalius, the acknowledged father of our art. Look at its size, and bear in mind that its thousand folio pages embrace only a special part of the human anatomy . . . Now, gentlemen . . .

(*He holds up a very small volume in his other hand.*)

. . . behold the advance of the age, the progress of science today, the *Pocket Anatomist,* said to contain the *whole* of Anatomy within the compass of three inches by two . . .

(*Reverently,* Doctor Knox *lays down the large volume on his lecturing table. With the greatest contempt, he casts the small volume from his platform. The students laugh uproariously. Then, the* Doctor *continues.*)

11

. . . At my dinner last night, I was asked why body-snatchers are known as Resurrectionists. The answer, Gentlemen, is simple. The removal of a body from the walled precincts of God's Acre was viewed by the superstitious and the credulous as nothing less than an interference with the plans of Providence and the Great Resurrection. So the poor ghoul of a body-snatcher became a 'Resurrectionist'. As Christians, you may well deplore the sacrilege of digging up the dead for anatomists to dissect. I am no platform drummer, no hawker of slogans, but I say that the Resurrectionists who dig up the dead and sell them to the Anatomical Schools are a direct result of the wrongness of the Law. The Law says that surgeons must possess a high degree of skill. And a surgeon cannot acquire that skill without working upon dead human beings. But the law also says that the only dead human beings we *can* work upon must come from the public gallows; a very uncertain, and meagre, supply. Legally, the hangman is our one provider. But he would have to hang all the *liars* in the City or all the men who are unfaithful to their wives, before there would be sufficient subjects for us. Therefore, we have to obtain our bodies illegally.

Gentlemen, you may begrudge the three pounds five shillings you have had to pay me for your First Course. Some of you may be begrudging me your five pounds nine shillings Perpetual Fee. But I myself, last term, had to pay out five hundred guineas to the Resurrectionists . . . Come, let us go to the Dissecting Rooms . . .

(The Students *disperse.)*

5
LOG'S

(It is a room in the lodging house kept by William Hare *and his wife. Offstage, in the inner, hidden room, a* Parish Carpenter *is nailing up a coffin.* Burke *and* Hare, *who stand at the entrance to the small adjoining room, are listening.)*

Hare. Hammer him in, hammer him in. Four pounds rent all dead in a box. Four pounds being nailed up ready to be put underground. At this rate, this lodging house will soon be running at a loss.

Burke. Now who would've thought old Donald could be so mean. Dying without a word, and owing you four pounds . . .

Hare. He didn't even have a penny piece hidden under the straw . . . I know; I looked; I got him out of his bed almost as soon as he'd stopped breathing, so as we could get someone else into it. Threepence a night would be too much to lose, on top of all the other.

Burke. You should ha' kept him alive. His pension was due next month. You'll never see it now.

Hare. If only he was alive again so that I could kill him with my hands . . . All he left was a bit of a broken pipe . . . And livin' here all these months on the fat of the land . . . Many's the night I've beaten the rats off him myself . . .

(Burke is slouching in a kind of self-pitying gloom, but Hare is half dancing with rage. The Parish Carpenter goes on hammering.)

. . . Four pounds gone! Four pounds of food and drink and bonnets gone! No more money for Hare! Hammer him in . . . Hammer him in!

(The Parish Carpenter appears in the doorway.)

The Parish Carpenter. And what do you think I'm doing? Pullin' him out?

(The Parish Carpenter returns to his task. Slowly, Hare's dancing fury dies; he swivels his eyes towards Burke; Burke looks back at him, and slowly through his mulish blood-shot stupidity he seems to understand.)

Burke *(In a heavy whisper).* Hammer him in . . . Hammer him in . . .

Hare *(Softly).* 'And what do you think I'm doing . . .'

(He speaks more loudly.)

. . . 'Pulling him out?' I've got to get that four pounds back somehow. Can you think of another way?

(The Parish Carpenter drives in a last nail, then he reappears in the doorway with his bag of tools.)

The Parish Carpenter. That's it, then. He's a' tucked up ready for the saulies.

Hare. 'A' tucked up ready for the saulies' . . . They can have him, man, as soon as they like to come for him.

The Parish Carpenter. I expect you'll be glad to be rid o' him. They'll be along, the now. Goodday to you, then.

Hare and **Burke** *(As if in a trance).* Good day to you, fellow . . . Good . . . day . . . to . . . you.

*(The **Parish Carpenter** goes off to his next Pauper Casketing.)*

Hare. Four pounds he owes me and ten pounds they'll give us for him. We can put tanner's bark, in the box, from the yard at the back.

Burke *(With a kind of sodden horror).* Body-snatchers!

Hare *(Calling).* Mag! Mag! Come here!

*(**Mrs. Hare** comes in, followed by **Helen M'Dougal**.)*

Mrs. Hare. What do you want?

Hare. Ye've got a big tea chest, there, in your back ben. What have you got in it?

Mrs. Hare. Only a few bits and clothes.

Hare. Well, get 'em out of it quickly, and bring it here. We've a use for it.

*(The **Women** go out again, and **Burke** and **Hare** enter the inner room, to deal with the coffin.)*

6
THE ANATOMY THEATRE

*(**Doctor Knox** is seen at the table from which he usually lectures. He is demonstrating, silently, to a group of **Students**. **Burke** and **Hare** approach from a distance, carrying a large tea-chest. Two **Students** pass them. **Hare** nudges **Burke**. **Burke** and **Hare** put down the tea-chest, and **Burke** follows the students.)*

Burke *(In a whining voice).* Beg your pardon me askin', Sirs, if it's not too much trouble for you, could you be telling me which the Academy is? We've a little matter of business . . .

*(The **Students** pause and turn round.)*

First Student. What Academy do you want?

Second Student. And what's the little business? . . .

14

(He sees the tea-chest a little way off, with **Hare**, *its attendant, winking and leering.)*

. . . Oh!

(He draws the **First Student**'s *attention to the tea-chest.)*

First Student. If it's a subject . . .

(**Burke** *cringes, and nods, and nods again.)*

. . . you've brought it to exactly the right place. This is Doctor Knox's. He'll pay you a better price than Munro.

Burke. Oh, yes, that was the name, Sirs, Munro, Sirs, Munro.

First Student. You let Doctor Knox have it. The porter will see to you if you wait here.

Burke. Oh, thank you, Sirs, thank you, my humblest thanks to you, Sirs . . .

(The two **Students** *walk off as* **David Paterson** *appears.)*

David Paterson. Yes?

Burke *(Ingratiatingly).* Two young gentlemen told us we could sell an article here . . . We got it in the tea-chest.

David Paterson. *Ah. . .* Wait here then, quietly. Don't move now.

(**David Paterson** *leaves* **Burke** *and* **Hare** *standing one at each side of the tea-chest, and approaches* **Doctor Knox**.*)*

Doctor Knox *(Demonstrating).* . . . It was Herophilus who first traced the arachnoid membrane into the ventricles of the brain, and . . .

David Paterson *(With an apologetic cough).* Doctor Knox, Sir . . .

Doctor Knox. What is it, Mr. Paterson?

David Paterson *(In a confidential voice).* There's a couple of new hands down by, Sir. They've brought . . .

Dcotor Knox *(Turning to the* **Students** *and interrupting* **David Paterson***).* Excuse me, gentlemen, you and Herophilus must wait a few moments . . .

(**David Paterson** *follows* **Doctor Knox** *to where* **Burke** *and* **Hare** *are waiting. The* **Doctor**, *taking no notice of them at all, goes to the tea-chest.* **David Paterson** *hurries to his side, cuts the ropes around the chest, and drags away some straw and rags.* **Doctor Knox** *looks inside. Then he straightens up, takes out a purse, and hands it to* **David Paterson**.*)*

15

... Give them seven pounds ten ...

(As **David Paterson** *opens the purse and counts out the money from it,* **Doctor Knox,** *for the first time, looks at* **Burke** *and* **Hare.)**

... What are your names?

Burke *(Stepping forward, toadyingly).* William Burke, Sir.

Doctor Knox. And the other?

*(***Hare** *smiles a long side smile, but he does not speak.)*

Burke. Hare, Sir.

Doctor Knox. If you have any more, let us have them.

(The **Doctor** *walks away. And* **David Paterson** *hands over the money to* **Burke***. Then he escorts* **Burke** *and* **Hare** *from the premises.)*

7
THE CITY MARKET PLACE

(Singing, again, and some noise of disorder. **Burke** *and* **Hare, Helen M'Dougal** *and* **Mrs. Hare** *are celebrating their new wealth.)*

Burke. For you, Nelly, love ...

(He pushes some coins across to **Helen M'Dougal** *from a big pile.)*

... All for yourself. For you, Mag ...

(He pushes some to **Mrs. Hare.***)*

... Hare and I share the rest.

(He divides the remaining coins. **Hare** *snatches his coins up.)*

Hare. A bottle, a bottle, another bottle!

(He goes away, for more drink.)

Helen M'Dougal *(Softly, in a kind of lumpish amazement).* Seven pounds ten, for an old man ... Seven pounds ten for an old man who had never seen so much money as this in all his life. I'll wager my share of it ... Seven pounds ten for an old man who wouldn't ha' known what to do with it, if he'd 'a' had it! ...

16

(Hare returns, with a bottle, and pours whisky into each of their mugs. Helen M'Dougal raises hers, in a barbaric toast.)

. . . Here's to the old man who was worth seven pounds ten!

Burke. Oh, the shame that he wasn't a young man!

(With their own kinds of laughter, they drink the toast. Then Burke calls 'Daft' Jamie across to them.)

. . . Here, Jamie! Take a mouthful of this! . . .

(He gives Jamie a drink from his mug.)

. . . Ye like your dram, when there's someone who'll give it you, don't you, Jamie?

Jamie. Oh, aye, I like fine a dram, but there's not many bodies as generous as you today. And d'ye ken why not?

Burke. D'ye ken why not what, Jamie?

Jamie. D'ye ken why there's not many bodies as generous as you today?

Hare. Why not, Jamie? Tell us, lad.

Jamie. 'A cause most of 'em is lying quite still in the old West Kirkyard, or at Pentland.

(Burke, Hare and the Womenfolk laugh uproariously.)

Hare. Well said, Jamie.

Burke. There's maybe a few that isn't, but it was a good old riddle, Jamie lad, just the same. Here's to Jamie! . . .

(Echoing 'Here's to Jamie!', his companions raise their glasses. At that moment, a Hawker comes into their view, carrying lace and other oddments. Burke snatches a shawl, and tosses a coin to the Hawker.)

. . . I'll have this . . .

(He takes more clothes.)

. . . and this . . . and this . . .

(And Hare decks himself with lace and minces around in a parody of a drunken woman. Then he, and the others, adorn Jamie. Burke gives the protesting Hawker more coins.)

Hare. Look at me, eh? . . . Look at me . . . Look at Daft Jamie there . . . Our own mothers wouldn't know us, would they, Jamie lad? . . .

Our own mothers wouldn't know us . . .

(Laughing hysterically, they prance off into the shadows as the singing and other sounds become fainter and fainter and fainter.)

8
LOG'S

*(It is the morning after the wild night before. **Burke** is despondent, having spent all his share of the money. **Hare** walks about the room, caged, his eyes darting sharply at every squalor.)*

Burke. And what do you think you'll find? Prowling like a cat. D'you think there's money in the old straw?

Hare. There's fat pigs in the yard outside.

Burke *(Not listening).* Drain the dry bottles, lick the floor, scrabble in the muck for a farthing. There's nothing, nothing.

Hare. Fat, juicy porkers waiting for the knife. How they'll squeeeel!

Burke. Shut your squeal. Ach, if old Donald was here, dying again!

Hare *(In a quiet voice).* Old Joseph's dying . . .

(There is silence for a moment.)

. . . Old Joseph coughs all night. Krawf! Krawf!

*(A longer silence. Then **Hare** speaks softly but clearly.)*

. . . It's awful tedious waiting for Old Joseph to die.

*(There is complete silence. Then there is the sound of the rustle of straw. Then **Old Joseph** appears from some other part of the house, followed closely by **Mrs. Hare**.)*

Burke. Come in here, Joseph. You aren't looking too well, are you?

Old Joseph. I feel bad, real bad. This fever . . .

Hare. Don't do the house any good, that fever of yours. Keeps people away, if they hear that there's fever in the place. You owe us money already, in a manner of speaking.

Burke. Here, have a dram of whisky. It will make you feel better. Give him some, Mag.

*(**Mrs. Hare** moves across and gives the **Old Man** a drink.)*

18

Old Joseph. Thank you, Mr. Burke. Thank you kindly . . .

(He drinks.)

. . . Ptchah! That's ardent liquid, that is.

Burke. And have another.

Old Joseph. Thank ye, Mr. Burke, no more.

Burke *(Threateningly).* Go on, have another. I tell you to.

Old Joseph *(Submissive).* Thank 'ee.

Hare. You aren't thinking of . . . ?

Burke. Why not? Remember what that man, said, 'If you have any more, let us have them'. . .'If you have any more, let us have them'. . . And seven pounds ten, we got for the last one.

Hare. But he was a goner. This one isn't.

Burke. This one isn't yet. But look at him. In one way of speaking 't would be a kindness to put him out of his misery, wouldn't it? He can't be enjoying himself, in that state of health. Give him another dram, Mag.

Old Joseph *(Weakly).* Mr. Burke!

Burke. Go on, drink it up, you old fool. It will make you feel better.

Hare. And in another manner o' speaking, 't would be no more than he deserves, coming to stay here, and then getting a fever.

Burke. Split even, Hare?

Hare. Eh?

Burke. Split even? Half the money to you, half to me?

Mrs. Hare. I want my share. This is my lodging house.

Hare. It was your lodging house.

Mrs. Hare. And I wants a pound, for the use of it.

Old Joseph. Oh, Mrs. Hare, my stomach . . . It do be paining me something terrible.

Burke. You won't be suffering wi' it much longer, Joseph, I promise you that. Now, Mrs. Hare is going to move you into this nice little room down here by yourself for a day or two, till the fever gets better. There's some good warm straw in there for you to lie on. You can be ill in there all by yourself. Give him a last dram, Mag.

Old Joseph *(In distress).* Oh-h-h . . .

*(***Burke*** signals to* **Mrs. Hare,** *who forces a last drink down the* **Old Man's** *throat and then takes him away to the inner room.)*

Burke. Now, we needs a pillow or something.

Hare. We needs a dram ourselves, too.

Burke. Aye, we needs a dram . . .

(They drink heartily.)

. . . Come on.

(The **Two Men** *go to the inner room.* **Mrs. Hare** *comes out. She listens for a moment, then she puts her hands over her ears and moves away.)*

9
THE ANATOMY THEATRE

(We catch a glimpse of **Doctor Knox,** *with top-hat and stick, very immaculate.* **David Paterson** *approaches him.)*

David Paterson. It's William Burke and Hare again, Sir. They've brought a new subject. It's an old man. He's not . . . very long dead. They want ten pounds, Sir.

Doctor Knox. Give it to them.

(The **Doctor** *walks on. His face is expressionless.)*

10
THE CITY MARKET PLACE

(Music. Darkness gathering deeper. The lights are coming on, but children still play on the cobbles; and from the alleys behind them, in the unseen courts and closes, come the voices of other children. And men and women stand about in shop and house and tavern doorways, drinking, talking, quarrelling. The simpleton, **'Daft' Jamie,** *is being taunted by a group of very small* **Savages,** *who are dancing round him in a ring.)*

The Smallest Savage. I'll fecht you, Jamie.

Jamie. Na, Na, I willna fecht. It's only bad boys that fecht . . .

(The **Smallest Savage** *gives* **Jamie** *a blow.* **Jamie** *moves off out of range.)*

. . . That wisna sare, man. Ye canna catch me.

The Savages. Ye're a scaredy, Daft Jamie! Ye're a scaredy, Daft Jamie! Cowardy coward custard, wants a dose of mustard!

Jamie. What way dae ye ca' me daft?

The Savages. Because ye are! Because ye are! Because ye are!

Jamie. I'm no', though. As sure's death, de'il tak' me, I'm no daft at 'a.

The Savages. Ye are! Ye are! Ye are!

*(***Doctor Knox*** is passing through the market place with* **Alexander Miller** *his assistant.* **Jamie** *runs away from the* **Savages**, *and over to* **Doctor Knox**. *The* **Doctor** *stops, and smiles at him.)*

Doctor Knox. Good evening, Jamie . . .

*(***Jamie*** smiles back delightedly, and bobs his head up and down.)*

. . . It's a cold night to be running about in the streets.

Jamie. It isn'a cold for Jamie . . . Not cold . . .

(Like a taught parrot, **Jamie** *gabbles.)*

. . . Jamie's never cold in September or November or December. Why not?

Doctor Knox *(Patiently).* Why not, Jamie? Why isn't Jamie cold in September or November or December?

Jamie. Because there's aye an ember in the month . . .

*(***Doctor Knox*** puts money gently into* **Jamie's** *hand.)*

Doctor Knox. Well done, Jamie. Here's a present for you, boy. Hold it in your hand. Don't lose it.

*(***Doctor Knox*** and* **Alexander Miller** *move on.)*

Jamie *(From behind them).* 'Night . . . 'night . . . Doctor Knox . . .

Doctor Knox. Now he'll hurry as fast as he can on his bent bones to the nearest tavern, and fuddle his few poor wits, and crack his crazed little jokes half remembered from the cradle. Oh, how the pious would lift their hands to heaven to think of a man giving money to an idiot so that he could get drunk and be warm and happy for an hour or two. Let him rather die a sober frozen idiot in the gutter! . . . Would you care to join me at dinner, Alexander? Or

21

are you due to visit the fair Jennie Bailey tonight?

Alexander Miller. Thank you, Robert. The delightful Miss Bailey is otherwise engaged, or I would be with her already.

Doctor Knox. Come on, then, Sir . . .

(They walk out of the market.)

11
LOG'S

*(***Mrs. Hare** *and* **Helen M'Dougal** *are preparing for a meal: that is, one of them, with an almost bristleless broom, is sweeping some broken glass into a corner: the other is laying out four pewter mugs. Suddenly, there is a noise of singing and stamping from outside and* **Hare** *dances in, a bottle under each arm. He winks and leers at the* **Women**, *nods and jerks his fingers at the direction from which he has appeared. And in staggers* **Burke**, *singing, with a* **Little Old Woman** *hanging, half falling, on his arm. She too is trying to sing.)*

Burke. And look what I've brought home, my doves. A pretty old woman with nowhere to sleep . . . have you, Granny? Nowhere to sleep but with us. Shall we give her a bed?

Helen M'Dougal. Where d'you find her?

*(***Hare** *is opening a bottle and pouring whisky into the mugs. He gives the* **Little Old Woman** *one.)*

Hare. Drink with Hare!

Burke. She was lying in the gutter like an old cabbage, weren't you, Granny? Her poor grey hairs dragging in the mud. And who should pick her up but kind Bill? . . .

*(***Burke** *gives the* **Little Old Woman** *some kind of a seat.)*

. . . There. The place of honour. Nothing's too good for her.

Mrs. Hare. What are you going to do?

Hare. Do? Drink!

Burke. Do? Drink with Granny. All night long . . .

(The **Little Old Woman** *titters and drinks. She nearly falls over, but* **Burke** *catches her and supports her.)*

. . . No harm must come to you now. You might have bumped your head . . .

(He speaks softly.)

. . . And then what'd the doctors think? . . .

*(***Hare** *skips over and takes the* **Little Old Woman's** *mug from her hand and pours whisky down her throat. She coughs and gasps.)*

Hare. Down she goes, Granny me darlin'.

Burke *(In a different voice, to* **Helen M'Dougal** *and* **Mrs. Hare***).* You two be running off on an errand.

Hare. You needn't be long.

Burke *(Slowly).* Go now . . .

(The **Women,** *without a word, and without looking at the* **Little Old Woman,** *fasten their shawls and go out.* **Burke** *speaks to the* **Little Old Woman** *as though to a child.)*

. . . Up you get, dear. Don't you want no more whisky? . . .

(Into her ear.)

. . . Whisky! Whisky!

(Trembling, the **Little Old Woman** *manages to regain some consciousness. As soon as she does,* **Hare,** *ready all the time, pours more whisky down her throat.)*

Burke. Give me the bottle . . .

*(***Hare** *hands it to him.* **Burke** *drinks from it. He passes the bottle back. He rubs the sweat off his forehead. Then he moves, unsteadily but heavily, closer to the* **Little Old Woman.***)*

. . . Come on, me lovey. Bye-byes for Gran-gran.

(Together, the **Two Men** *take the* **Little Old Woman** *to the inner room.)*

12
THE ANATOMY THEATRE

(Alexander Miller is busy with some Students, *as* Burke *and* Hare, *without any instruction from* David Paterson, *move in with a large tea-chest.* Alexander Miller *sees them, and beckons* David Paterson *over to him.)*

Alexander Miller. Who are the dapper gentlemen?

David Paterson. William Burke and his friend Hare, Sir. They're new hands . . . but they're getting pretty regular. They ask for ten pounds.

(Alexander Miller goes across and looks into the tea-chest. Then he nods his head.)

Alexander Miller. That'll do . . .

(Then he speaks so that only David Paterson *can hear.)*

. . . If any more bodies call, tell them I'm at the theatre with Doctor Knox. Good evening, David.

(The Men *go their separate ways.)*

13
LOG'S

*(*Mrs. Hare *and* Helen M'Dougal *are tidying the room, sweeping dirt into corners, and stopping to drink from a bottle placed conveniently in the centre of the room.*

We hear, from outside, the sound of a knock on the door.

Mrs. Hare *wipes her lips on her shawl and tucks the bottle inside her thick layers of clothes.)*

Mrs. Hare. More lodgers!

(She goes out of the room. Helen M'Dougal *tipsily tidies herself, spits in her hand to help straighten a hanging lock of stiff hair.*

Then Mrs. Hare *comes back with a big, old, ragged* Beggar Man *shuffling behind her, all dirt and hair, like a tame, tired, time- and whip- and weather-beaten bear.)*

Mrs. Hare. You can sleep in any bed you like, Dad, for twopence a
night. Clean and comfy.

Helen M'Dougal. Are you alone?

(The **Old Man** *nods his head.)*

Mrs. Hare. All alone in the world? Nobody to care about you at all?

(The **Old Man** *shakes his head.)*

Mrs. Hare. Ach, isn't it a shame . . . Nobody to care if you're alive or
dead . . .

*(***Mrs. Hare** *looks at* **Helen M'Dougal.***)*

Helen M'Dougal. Let the old man have a doss down for a penny, Mag.

(And **Mrs. Hare** *takes the* **Old Man's** *luggage– which is wrapped
up in a handkerchief– and they each hold an arm and lead him
over to the door of the inner room.)*

14

THE ANATOMY THEATRE

*(***Doctor Knox** *approaches his platform table alone, and with his
usual careful deliberation starts to rehearse a lecture.)*

Doctor Knox. Gentlemen. Are we to be told that the Kafir is a savage
because he lives in the wilds, and that John Bull is the happy
creature of civilization because he wears breeches, learns the
catechism, and cheats his neighbours? I say, Gentlemen, that the
Kafir, in his equatorial hut . . .

*(***Doctor Knox** *starts as he sees that* **Alexander Miller** *has
approached him silently.)*

. . . You make your way about very softly, Mr. Miller.

Alexander Miller. They've got Jennie Bailey downstairs.

Doctor Knox. Jennie Bailey? And who can blame them? 'Tis a beautiful
slut with a bold eye and–if you don't mind me saying so–a tongue
like a drunken horse-thief's. But what might she be doing downstairs? I am sure, Mr. Miller, that she is an expert in Anatomy,
but her knowledge might not be sufficiently academic . . . Or has
she come merely to entertain?

25

Alexander Miller. She has come, Sir, to be dissected.

Doctor Knox. How very generous of her. I did not think that science was so near her heart. Does she wish to be dissected alive?

Alexander Miller. She is *dead.*

Doctor Knox. That is carrying scientific generosity to its furthest limit.

Alexander Miller. She was murdered.

Doctor Knox *(Sharply).* Who says so?

Alexander Miller. She was murdered.

Doctor Knox. Are there signs of violence upon the body?

Alexander Miller. She was murdered by two paid thugs of yours: Burke and Hare. I believe that she was smothered to death in such a way as to leave no signs. I saw her last night after the theatre. She was well and gay. There are no signs of violence upon her body.

Doctor Knox. Thugs of mine, Mr. Miller? Do you remember that you yourself paid them for the last subject they brought?

Alexander Miller. She was murdered. I saw her . . .

(Slowly, rememberingly.)

. . . She had a red shawl on.

Doctor Knox. Indisputable evidence that she was murdered. She should have worn a white shawl, for purity. And what if she was murdered, Mr. Miller? We are anatomists, not policemen; we are scientists, not moralists. Do I, I, care if every lewd and abandoned woman of the streets comes to the end she has probably richly deserved? She served no purpose in life that would have justified an extended old age. Let her serve her purpose in death.

Alexander Miller. You hired Burke and Hare to murder her as you hired them to murder the others.

Doctor Knox. I need bodies. They brought bodies. I pay for what I need. I do not hire murderers . . .

(For a moment, the two men stare at each other, in a silent conflict of wills. Then, with a low sob, **Alexander Miller** *turns to go. Before he can pass out of earshot,* **Doctor Knox** *makes a final thrust.)*

. . . Oh, Mr. Miller . . .

(That stops the other man.)

. . . I think that before the body is put into the brine bath, a drawing should be made of it, do not you? Shall we not allow posterity to share our exhilaration at the sight of such perfect physical beauty? I should be much obliged if you yourself would perpetuate on paper the loveliness of this poor clay, Mr. Miller. We know your skill with the pencil. God should have made you an artist. He did the next best thing: he gave you a very vivid imagination . . .

(And **Doctor Knox** *chuckles grimly as* **Alexander Miller** *strides out of the Anatomy Theatre.)*

15
LOG'S

(We see, in a corner, the pile of old rags and bones. It is far higher than when we last saw it.

      Mrs. Hare *lies half on, half off, a heap of straw.* **Helen M'Dougal** *is listening to the squealing of pigs in the yard outside. Then* **Hare** *lurches in, with* **Daft Jamie.***)*

Helen M'Dougal *(In a shocked whisper).* Not . . . Daft Jamie!

Hare *(To* **Helen M'Dougal***).* Them pigs is too loud . . . It sounds like a killing . . . Bring out a bottle for Jamie . . . Sit down there, Jamie.

*(***Jamie** *smiles at* **Helen M'Dougal** *as she brings out a bottle.)*

Jamie. He bought me twa drinks, at the Old Dun Cow . . . And he bought me snuff.

*(***Hare** *takes the bottle from* **Helen M'Dougal** *and carries it over to* **Jamie** *and gives it him and watches him drink. We see* **Jamie's** *face as he drinks: drunkenly made beautiful.)*

Hare *(To* **Helen M'Dougal***).* Go round the shebeens and find your man. Tell him there's business . . .

*(***Helen M'Dougal** *goes to leave the room. She looks over her shoulder at* **Jamie.***)*

. . . Would ye be having some more, Jamie? Ach, it's you and me could drink the sea dry, and eat the fishes . . .

*(***Hare** *speaks ingratiatingly.)*

. . . and cuddle the mermaids and dance a jig and play the penny

27

whistle, and . . . and . . .

Jamie. I've seen a shark.

Hare. You could wrestle the shark and toss him over your head like a pound of cat's-meat . . . You're strong, Jamie.

Jamie. I know a riddle.

Hare. Tell Hare your riddle . . . Another drink, eh, Jamie?

Jamie. In what month of the year dae the ladies talk least?

Hare. Oh, that's a good one. In what month of the year do the ladies talk least? And what month would that be, Jamie?

Jamie. The month of February, because there wiz least days in it.

*(***Hare*** raises his head and yelps with laughter and slaps his thigh. Delighted,* **Jamie** *splutters and crows.)*

Hare. Tell Hare another riddle, Jamie . . . another riddle.

Jamie. I can tell you a riddle that nobody knows and nobody can guess it.

Hare. What is it, Jamie?

Jamie. Though I black an' dirty am,
    An' black as black can be,
  There's many a lady that will come
    And by the hand tak' me.
Now you can't guess that.

Hare. Ah, no, Jamie, I can't guess that fickly one. Who learned you all those fickly guesses?

Jamie. It wiz my half step-mither . . . Oh, she wiz a cunning old body! Oh, she used to be as cunning as a kitten when we wiz all sitting beside her round the fireside. She used to tell us a million million million funny stories, but I don't remember them all.
'Though I black and dirty am,
  An . . . '

Hare. I know! The answer's a tea kettle.

Jamie *(Almost in tears).* Somebody told you.

Hare. Nobody told me, Jamie, I guessed it, honest. But tell us another one, Royal Jamie, and I'll not guess it this time, an' . . .

(Proffering the bottle.)

. . . an' we'll drink . . . an' we'll drink . . . an' we'll drink . . .

*(***Hare's*** voice fades as he sees that* **Helen M'Dougal** *has returned*

28

without Burke. He speaks to her.)

. . . Where is he?

Helen M'Dougal. He won't come. He says his hands have worked enough. He says there's devils in his hands . . . He's drunk himself daft again, like he was when he was on his knees in the street, prayin' and shoutin' . . . He says he wishes he was workin' again, on the roads, on the canals, anywhere.

Hare. You should ha' told him . . .

Helen M'Dougal. I asked him if he wanted us all to starve while he blathered and wept his eyes out . . .

Hare. Go back, and don't ye return here without him, even if ye've got to drag him here, d'ye understand? . . .

*(**Helen M'Dougal** looks thoroughly frightened, but she has to obey. As she goes out, **Hare** turns his attention back to Jamie.)*

. . . And when Mr. Burke comes back, oh, we'll have fun and singing . . . It's he's got a voice that will send you to sleep like your mother's . . . And oh, the joking and the riddles . . .

*(**Burke** is standing at the threshold, with his shoulders back and his head held high. There is something almost of dignity about him: something that might suggest he is about to make a sacrifice. And when he speaks, it is without the usual blarneying whine; a horror that has reached him has deepened the tone of his voice.)*

Burke *(Slowly)*. Make Mag go . . .

*(**Hare** moves across the room in two cat-padded jumps and pinches his **Wife** awake.*

*She looks round the room, thick with sleep. She sees **Jamie** smiling at every one and no one; she sees the malicious face of **Hare** above her; she sees **Burke** grim in the doorway. Behind him is **Helen M'Dougal**.*

*Sober in a second, and frightened, she scrambles to escape. **Burke** does not move; she has to squeeze herself past him, keeping her body as far away from his as she can.)*

Burke. Get outside . . .

*(But he is staring at **Jamie**. He speaks slowly to the poor daft boy.)*

. . . You mustn't be frightened, Jamie . . .

(He takes a step forward.)

. . . It'll all be over soon. No more bein' hungry . . .

(His movements are almost those of a priest.)

. . . No . . . more . . . cold . . . No . . . more . . . children . . . to . . . taunt . . . ye . . . in . . . the . . . market . . . place . . .

*(Bewildered, but still smiling, **Jamie** is taken by the two **Men** to the inner room. The two **Women** stand quite still. They are tensed, waiting, close together. And from the inner room comes **Jamie's** scream.*

The scream mounts, breaks, and bursts out again. There is the crash of a falling chair.

*And now it is not a scream that comes from beyond the door but a terrified howling: and with it the sound of a deeper voice: **Burke's** voice—the voice of the damned inarticulately praying. And with it the smashing of wood, and glass breaking.*

Then one scream destroys all other sounds.

The women put their hands over their ears, and run from the room.)

ACT TWO

I

LOG'S

(Mrs. Hare comes in, takes a long drink, and is disturbed by a knocking at the alley door. She brings in a middle-aged man and a woman—we shall know them as Gray and Mrs. Gray. Mrs. Gray is carrying a baby, wrapped in a shawl.)

Mrs. Hare. You'll be wanting a bed? They're twopence.

Gray. Bed . . .

Mrs. Hare. Wait here.

(She goes to the inner room. Mrs. Gray looks round the sordid lodging-house with distaste.)

Mrs. Gray. It's a poor, dirty place.

Gray. It's got a roof . . .

Mrs. Gray. I think I'd rather be on the roads, sleeping in the hedge in the cold . . .

(She stops talking as Mrs. Hare returns.)

Mrs. Hare. There's nobody sleeping at all here now, but us . . . You can take your fancy where you sleep, out of the whole house . . .

(She looks closely at Gray and Mrs. Gray.)

. . . You're strangers here . . .

Gray. Strangers everywhere . . .

Mrs. Hare. You're from the roads?

(Gray nods.)

Mrs. Gray. I think we won't be troubling you for a bed . . . It's dark here . . .

Mrs. Hare. It's darker on the roads. With no one you know in the world, and no one to take care of you . . . I'll make the beds a penny each. What names d'you go by?

31

Gray. Mr. and Mrs. Gray.

Mrs. Gray. We're respectable people . . .

Mrs. Hare. We're all respectable here. Just my husband and me. He's
in the way of a merchant . . . I'll show you the sleeping places . . .

(She leads the **Grays** *out.)*

2

THE ANATOMY THEATRE

(**Alexander Miller** *and* **David Paterson** *are alone in an atmosphere
of gloom and suspicion.)*

Alexander Miller. Who brought the subjects in, Paterson? There's no
need to ask.

David Paterson. Burke and Hare, Sir, Burke and Hare.

Alexander Miller. What can we do? . . . What can we do? . . . What can
we do? . . . But keep quiet.

David Paterson. Nothing, but keep quiet, if keep quiet we must.

Alexander Miller. There were no marks of violence on the body . . .
were there?

David Paterson. No marks of violence.

Alexander Miller. If we could get him to go away, at once. Out of the
country. I owe him a great deal. I would not care to see him . . .
hanged.

David Paterson. Could ye no' speak to him, about it?

Alexander Miller. Speak to him about it? I have, and that. And what
did he say to me? He called me a rumour breeder. He said that I
had fallen in love with a pretty face, and that that was affecting
my judgment. He said that if he ever takes up assassination, he
will start with the surgeons in this city and work up to the gutter . . .
And when I told him it was Daft Jamie, a poor natural that
everyone in the city knows, all he said was that Jamie was a
consumptive and an epileptic, and that it was a wonder he hadn't
been found dead years ago . . . And then . . . And then . . .

(The memory is too much for him.)

. . . Oh, God . . .

32

David Paterson. And then, Mr. Miller?

Alexander Miller. And then he said: 'Mr.Miller, go down and cut up the body and put it in the brine baths. Be careful you don't fall in yourself—that's a very elegant suit you're wearing' . . . His hands are as red as Macbeth's . . .

3

THE CITY MARKET PLACE

(The Market Place is crowded, and noisy. The atmosphere of this scene can be as nearly as possible that of a dream, with scraps of apparently unrelated conversation overheard against a drifting background. The first voice we hear is **Burke's**. *He has been trying unsuccessfully to drown his worries.)*

Burke. There's devils in my hands. Let me go, my hands! . . .

(His shouts alarm a group of old women and children.)

. . . Don't be frightened . . . There's nothing to lose . . . It's all lost.

A Random Voice. And where d'you get all the money so quick? You're rich, you're *rich*, you're . . .

Burke. Ach, I done a little smuggling; a little bit o' drink on the sly . . .

Another Random Voice. And where d'you get all the money so quick? You're *rich*, you're . . .

Helen M'Dougal. Oh, I've been left a property in the country.

A Third Voice. And where d'you get all the money . . .?

Mrs. Hare. Oh, Burke's the favourite of a great lady . . . Twenty pounds a visit she gives him . . .

Children. Where's Jamie? Where's Daft Jamie?

More Children. Gone, gone . . .

The Random Voice. Where's Jennie? Where's Jennie Bailey?

Burke. Gone, gone . . .

Hare. Drink with Hare . . . Drink . . . Drink . . .

(Part of the stage can at this point represent the outside of a **Grocer's Shop.** *Our attention is directed towards an* **Old Woman** *standing there, wrapped in pieces of the discarded clothing of*

33

the other poor. We shall know her eventually as **Mrs. Docherty.***)*

The Grocer. For the last time, I don't know a Docherty . . .

Mrs. Docherty. William Boylan Docherty . . .

The Grocer. I don't know a Docherty, I've never known a Docherty, I never want to know a Docherty . . .

Mrs. Docherty. From County Donegal . . . He came over two years ago and a half . . . He's a tall, dark boy . . . The lobes of his ears is pointed . . .

(**Burke** *approaches and stands, listening.)*

The Grocer. 'What's the time of the day?' . . . 'Can you give me a wooden box?' . . . 'My sister's fallen under a hay cart—can you lend me a penn'orth of brandy' . . . 'Have you seen a Docherty?' . . . Will nobody ever *buy* anything?

Mrs. Docherty. Could you spare me a bite o' bread, then?

(The **Grocer** *controls himself as* **Burke,** *with a winning smile, comes closer.)*

Burke *(To* **Mrs. Docherty***).* Did I hear you say 'Docherty'? That was my mother's name.

Mrs. Docherty. From Ardara, Donegal?

Burke *(Amazed).* Ardara, Donegal! My mother's town! And would *your* name be—Docherty, too?

The Grocer. *Her* name's Docherty, she's *looking* for a Docherty, and now your *mother's* name is Docherty . . .

Burke *(Still looking at the* **Old Woman,** *but speaking to the* **Grocer***).* Bring her some dew . . . Bring us a whole jug of mountain dew . . .

(The **Grocer** *goes off to get some drink.* **Burke** *continues to speak affectionately to* **Mrs. Docherty.***)*

. . . Cousin Docherty . . . Faith, what a day of all days! I'm walking along gay as a thrush, I'm fragrant with the sweet smell of money, tonight's Hallowe'en when the witches fly and the whisky pours like rain, and who should I meet on top of it all but a Docherty from Ardara! . . .

(The **Grocer** *returns and hands an earthenware jug to* **Burke.** **Burke,** *tossing coins carelessly across, pays for it, but he does not take his eyes off* **Mrs. Docherty.***)*

Mrs. Docherty. It's my son for I'm looking all over, Sir . . .

Burke *(Emphatically).* Cousin.

Mrs. Docherty *(Hesitatingly).* . . . Cousin . . .

Burke. And we'll find your son for you if we have to pull the town down and scramble among the cobbles . . . You come with me, Cousin . . . You're as welcome as sunlight . . . I'll buy you a present for Hallowe'en, and I'll take you back to my fine house and we'll kick up a din like all Donegal drunk . . .

*(**Burke**, with a jug and **Mrs. Docherty**, moves resolutely away in the direction of* **Log's**.*)*

The Grocer *(With an awful resignation).* Hallowe'en!

4
LOG'S

(There is laughter, and snatches of singing, and a jig tune played on a penny whistle.

    Hare *and* **Mrs. Hare** *are dancing arm in arm, and singing.*

    Burke *is leaning back against a table, playing a whistle. There are cups and mugs on the table, bottles, and the earthenware jug.* **Helen M'Dougal** *and the lodger* **Gray** *are beating jig-time on the littered floor.* **Burke's Brother** *is a guest.*

    Then **Hare** *takes* **Mrs. Docherty** *by the arm and starts dancing with her.* **Mrs. Docherty** *is gay as an old cat.* **Hare** *is smiling and possessive.*

    Mr. Gray, *with a look of bemused contentment, is soaking pieces of bread in the earthenware jug and eating them;* **Mrs. Gray,** *disapproving, complains through the singing, the dancing, the floor-beating, and the whistling.)*

Mrs. Gray. Oh, the noise, it'll wake all the neighbours . . .

Burke's Brother. They wouldn't wake tonight if you set their clothes on fire . . . All the city's drunk . . .

Mrs. Gray *(To Gray).* And stop eatin' bread and gin; it's bad for the stomach.

Hare. It's Hallowe'en . . .

Burke's Brother. It isn't us who's only making the din. You listen now . . . Shh!

(Burke's Brother raises his hand. For a moment the room is quiet. The dancers pause. From outside we hear the noise of drunken singing, and voices bawling and brawling.

Then Burke begins to play again, and Hare and Mrs. Docherty dance again, and Burke's Brother and Mrs. Hare sing, and Helen M'Dougal, by now almost incapable of speech, goes on thumping.)

Gray. Bread and gin's good for the stomach.

Mrs. Gray. You'll be waking the children, that's what'll happen next, with your caterwauling and your bang-bangs, and your . . .

(Burke stops playing.)

Burke. And can't a man have a party now in honour of his cousin?

Gray. And rum and spuds is good . . .

Burke *(To Mrs. Gray).* You're an auld spoil-sport, Mrs. Gray, you'd stop the dead dancin' on Judgment Day . . .

(Mrs. Gray's Baby, in the inner room, begins to scream. Mrs. Gray goes out to it, but the screaming continues.)

Burke. Now that's a baby that likes good music . . .

(He raises his penny whistle and plays again. Mrs. Gray is brought back by the noise of the dancing and singing and stamping that follows.)

Mrs. Gray. For the Lord's sake now, is this a lodging house or a wake?

(Burke is about to shout something rude at her, but he controls himself and, instead, nods to Mrs. Hare. She totters across to Mrs. Gray.)

Mrs. Hare. Ach, the poor creature. It screams like it swallowed a pin . . . And Burke'll be playing his whistle all night.

(Burke plays a few more bars on the whistle and dances a lonely jig.)

Mrs. Gray. All night? Then whatever . . .

Mrs. Hare. And there'll not be a breath of peace . . .

(She speaks in a wheedling voice.)

. . . Now why don't you take the child away for the night? Burke's brother here will give you a place to rest, and a plate of food in

36

the morning . . . Won't you, Sheamus, in your lodging?

Burke's Brother. Ay, I'll be glad of a bit of company, wi' the speerits around.

Mrs. Hare. And Burke and us'll stay singing with old Mrs. Docherty till we a' fall down . . .

(The **Baby** *screams louder than ever.)*

Mrs. Gray. Come on with ye, Mr. Gray, give me a hand with the baby. We'll need wrap it in plenty of warm clothes.

Gray. I don't want to go out in the cold.

Mrs. Gray. You and your bread and gin!

Burke's Brother. 'Tis only a couple of steps from here, Mrs. Gray. You'll be there, before the babby has had time to know it's been out of its cradle and under the night sky.

*(*Mrs. Gray *goes to fetch the Baby.)*

Hare. It's glad I'll be to be shot of them, too . . . turning the place into a rowdy house, with their boxing and their screaming and their carrying on . . .

Gray. Boxing? Who has been boxing? Save for my wife, that has been correcting the child when it has needed to be corrected . . .

Mrs. Hare *(Placatingly).* That's enough now, Mr. Gray . . .

*(*Mrs. Gray *returns with the* Baby. Mrs. Hare *speaks to her.)*

. . . I think you're very wise to go, my dear. There's no knowing what pranks Mr. Hare and Mr. Burke'll be up to to-night.

Burke's Brother. This way, Mrs. Gray.

(The Grays *are ushered from the room by* Mrs. Hare *and* Helen M'Dougal—Burke's Brother *going ahead to show them the way.)*

Burke. Now, dew! Dew from the mountains of Old Ireland!

(Mugs are filled, and a toast is drunk.)

All Present. To Hallowe'en!

*(*Burke *and* Hare *dance in turn with* Mrs. Docherty, *while* Mrs. Hare *and* Helen M'Dougal *keep the jig rhythm going, wildly.*

Then Hare *dances* Mrs. Docherty *through into the inner room.*

Mrs. Hare *and* Helen M'Dougal *keep the dance going,*

37

*together, but they are plainly trying to hear what is happening
in the inner room.*

After a few moments, **Burke** *and* **Hare** *reappear, without*
Mrs. Docherty*. The four dance, changing partners once or twice,
then they reel off variously into the shadows.*

*The stage is empty, as midnight chimes, and All Hallows'
Even is over.)*

5
LOG'S

*(A cold light, rising gradually until the room is fully illuminated,
shows that it is morning.*

*There is no one in the room, but we can see clearly a fouled
straw-heap on the floor, and the thrown-away bottles and the
flung scraps of clothes, and the broken glass and the drying pools
of drink and piled boots and rubbish in one corner.*

Then **Hare** *enters, and sits down, and pours himself a drink.)*

Hare. The snow won't ever stop. It's like the last day . . .

*(His voice, and his heavy, measured movements suggest the
anticlimax after the previous evening's festivities. He calls,
loudly.)*

. . . MAG! . . .

(There is no answer.)

. . . MAG, BLAST YER!

(Still no answer. Then, in a drowsy voice from off-stage.)

Mrs. Hare. What d'you want?

(She comes into the room wearily, takes a drink, and sits down.)

Hare. I wants something to eat . . .

(She yawns.)

. . . I wants something to eat, I tell you. What is there?

Mrs. Hare. Nothin' much. We had it yesterday. Don't you remember?

Hare. Yesterday . . .

38

(There is a moment's silence, as he reviews the events of the day before.)

. . . Can't we have some today?

Mrs. Hare. I'll get something, presently . . .

(She shows little inclination to do so. Yawning.)

. . . It's snowing.

(There is a loud knock. **Hare** *leaps to his feet.* **Mrs. Hare** *goes to admit the callers, who turn out to be* **Gray** *and* **Mrs. Gray.***)*

Hare *(With a frightening smile).* You frightened us.

Mrs. Hare. You're early.

Mrs. Gray. I been up and about since dawn; the baby wouldn't fall to sleep at all—it screamed like things were after it.

Mrs. Hare. What have you come for so early?

Mrs. Gray. I come to look for the child's clothes. I left them here last night. And I come for our bits and pieces . . . It's time we're moving.

*(***Mrs. Gray** *looks round the room. She pulls out a clay pipe from her wrappings and puts it in her mouth. Then she bends down and searches among the scraps of clothes on the floor.)*

Hare *(Harshly).* Get away from that straw with your old pipe . . . You'll have the room blazing!

*(***Mrs. Gray** *takes an involuntary step backward.)*

Gray. Where's that Mrs. Docherty? She was a very gay old woman, dancin' at her age like a nanny-goat.

Mrs. Hare. She was ow'r gay with Hare. She was very fashous during the night, so I gave her a kick in the seat and set her to the door.

Mrs. Gray. You set the old body to the door? In the snow?

Mrs. Hare. Ay. I tumbled her out of the house in the middle o' the night. She was a fashous old Irish limmer.

Gray *(With a side look at* **Mrs. Gray***).* I like a gay old woman . . .

Hare. Get out o' my room! Go on! Get out wi' you! . . . Take your reeky scraps of rubbish and get out! I don't want to see you nor your yelpin', snivellin' brat again, d'you understand? . . . GET OUT!

*(***Hare** *does not move, but his stillness is more menacing than*

39

movement. **Gray** *and* **Mrs. Gray** *go out. As they go,* **Mrs. Gray** *whines):*

Mrs. Gray. I want my little boy's stockings . . .

*(***Hare** *is alone with* **Mrs. Hare.***)*

Hare. The snow's falling heavier. The world's cold . . .

(He shivers, and pulls his coat closer about him.)

. . . It's cold in hell today. The fires are out . . .

*(***Mrs. Hare** *looks at him in uncomprehending silence.)*

. . . Nothing can burn me any more. I'm a cold man, Mag. I'm numb all over, like an old dead finger-nail. No more dancing and singing . . .

(He shivers again, and moves as if to look out of a window at the snow.)

. . . Burke and I got work to do. I'll go see if he's feeding the swine. You go and get me something to eat.

(He goes out, followed by the strangely silent **Mrs. Hare.** *For a moment, the room is empty. Then* **Mrs. Gray** *comes back, very quietly, and looks at the emptiness. She whispers over her shoulder)*

Mrs. Gray. They've gone.

(And **Gray** *comes in, nervously glancing behind him and on every side.)*

Gray. Find the stockings and things and let's be out of the house.

*(***Mrs. Gray** *is down on her knees now by the pile of straw and old clothes. She rummages through it.)*

Mrs. Gray. Who wanted to come to this house? I said it was bad. I could smell the badness as I come in. It's nothing but drinking and howling all night . . .

(Suddenly she stops in her scrabbling search through the pile of straw and clothes and lifts up a crumpled dress.)

. . . It's the old woman's dress.

Gray. How'd she be walking in the streets in the snow without her dress?

Mrs. Gray. It's the old woman's dress. I mind the colour.

(She starts to search among the pile again.)

Gray. A body doesna walk in the streets without her . . .

*(***Mrs. Gray*** *lifts up a ragged shawl.)*

Mrs. Gray. And here's her little patchy shawl . . .

(Now she is worrying the straw and clothes, like a dog on a scent.)

. . . And here's her . . .

(And **Mrs. Gray** *screams. She has seen a naked human arm in the pile. She springs up and stands looking down at the straw and the clothes and the arm.*
The scream stops.
Gray *bends down and moves more of the straw and the clothes to one side.)*

Gray. The gay old woman! Her face is a' slimy.

*(***Mrs. Gray*** *moves as if she is about to rush out of the room.*
Gray *moves as if he is about to follow her.*
But **Mrs. Hare** *is standing in their way.)*

Mrs. Hare. Where are you going? What have you seen?

Mrs. Gray. Let me out, she's dead . . .

Mrs. Hare. She died in her sleep . . .

Gray. Her mouth's blood . . .

Mrs. Gray. For the love o' Mary . . .

Mrs. Hare. She died in her sleep, I tell you . . .

Mrs. Gray. Let me out . . .

*(***Mrs. Hare*** *tears inside her apron, pulls out a purse, opens it. She pushes a handful of coins towards* **Mrs. Gray.)**

Mrs. Hare. Nobody knows her, nobody'll claim her, you mustn't tell a word . . .

Gray. Stand away . . .

Mrs. Hare. She died like a baby . . .

Mrs. Gray. You killed her in there last night . . .

Mrs. Hare. You mustn't tell a word, mercy, quiet, quiet . . . Hare'll give you ten pounds, ten pounds a week . . .

(Gray thrusts Mrs. Hare aside. Mrs. Gray runs past Mrs. Hare. Gray runs out after her. Mrs. Hare cries out after them.)

. . . Ten pounds! Ten pounds!

6
THE ANATOMY THEATRE

(Doctor Knox addresses the empty room as though there were a gathering of students in it, turning from one invisible listener to another.)

Doctor Knox. Gentlemen . . . Gentlemen, let us to-day dissect the human conscience. Lay it on the slab. Open it up.

You see? The liver of the conscience is knobbled by emotional excesses.

The veins of the conscience are full of bad blood.

The heart of the conscience palpitates like a snared rabbit's.

In short, gentlemen, the conscience is a very unhealthy subject.

There is right and wrong, gentlemen, just as there is right and left. Mine is the *right* direction. The fact that the majority would consider it the *wrong* direction only substantiates my opinion that I am right . . .

(There is a quiet knock.)

. . . Stay out . . .

(David Paterson comes in.)

. . . I see, Sir, that to keep you out I should have said 'Come in'.

David Paterson. Burke and Hare, Sir.

Doctor Knox. Indeed? Must I laugh, weep, tear my hair, swoon for ecstacy . . . ?

David Paterson. They've brought a body, Sir.

Doctor Knox. I did not expect that they would bring a soul.

David Paterson *(Suggestively)*. They bring so many subjects, Sir . . . Sixteen or more up till to-day . . . and always fresh . . .

Doctor Knox. They are corpse-diviners. Or, as some have green fingers for gardening, so they have black fingers for death. Do you expect the dead to walk here, David? They need assistance. Burke and Hare provide that assistance. Have Mr. Miller pay them. And then ask Mr. Miller to step up here to see me.

David Paterson. Yes, Sir.

(David Paterson, with a side glance at Doctor Knox, goes out. And Doctor Knox, alone, again speaks in a soft voice to his unseen audience.)

Doctor Knox. The professors of this fair city regard themselves as a 'royal family of the intellect'. My attitude to society has never endeared me to them. 'A man who can be so persistently and obnoxiously rude to his elders and intellectual betters', they say of me, 'would think nothing of murdering his own children for a penny piece' . . .

(Alexander Miller approaches, unobtrusively.)

. . . Ah, Miller, I asked you to step up, because I wish you to see the letter I am sending off today to the Caledonian Mercury, and the Weekly Chronicle. Will you take a glance at it? . . .

(Doctor Knox hands a sheet of paper to Alexander Miller. He goes on talking before Miller has had a chance to read all that is written on the paper.)

. . . If that does not upset some apple-carts, I shall believe that the apples have been glued on like the coco-nuts in coco-nut shies; if this does not help to change the idiotic laws that apply to our profession, I shall run amok; I shall send my incompetent rivals my Christmas Greetings, and I will sign them 'Yours in Homage'; I shall place my spiritual welfare in the hands of the most unctuous bishop I can find, and have my seat reserved in hell.

Alexander Miller. I tell you, this isn't the time to attack.

(He hands the letter back to Doctor Knox.)

Doctor Knox. The national anthem of the rabbit world.

Alexander Miller. If you publish that letter now, attacking the system by which the medical schools get their bodies, you'll be raising a question you might have some difficulty in answering yourself.

Doctor Knox. Am I still a Doctor Bluebeard to you, then, you terrified old lady? Do I spend my nights a-murdering?

Alexander Miller. I do not know, Sir, what you do with your nights. I do not imagine that you can *sleep*. But I do know that *Burke* and *Hare* are murderers. It is only my respect for you, and my great obligations, and my *cowardice*, that have stopped me from running out of this murder school and telling the whole city what I know and what I guess . . . Even so, there are rumours. *I* have not spread them. But the deaths of Jennie Bailey and of Daft Jamie have not passed *quite* unnoticed. Rumours are contagious.

Doctor Knox. So are scabies. To destroy them you do not wear the armour of defence, you wield the weapon of sulphur ointment. And, by God, there's sulphur in this letter!

*(Waving it, the **Doctor** goes off to send it on its way. **Alexander Miller** follows him, gesturing vainly.)*

7
THE CITY MARKET PLACE

*(There is great excitement in the market place, as might be expected when the Law is being invoked in such a lawless place. **Gray** and **Mrs. Gray** are talking to a **Policeman**. There are shouts of:*
> 'Where's Jennie Bailey?'
> 'Where's Daft Jamie?'
> 'What's happened to the Bailey girl?'
> 'What's happened to the poor daftie?'
> 'Where's Ludovici and his mice?')

Gray *(To the **Policeman**).* There was blood all over her face . . .

Policeman. Aye. I've seen them like that, afore.

Mrs. Gray. And her poor lips were blue and her eyes were staring out as though somebody'd pressed 'em with his thumbs . . .

More Shouts. Where's Jennie Bailey?
> Where's Daft Jamie? . . . . etc.

Singing. Up the alley and down the street,
> Dan's the man sells bones and meat,
> Jennie's the maid who milks the cow,
> And Dan's the man who shows her how.

Gray. She said she came from Donegal . . .

Policeman. The 'dead woman' told ye she'd come from Donegal?

(Wild laughter from the Bystanders.*)*

Gray. No, no, Sir, she said she'd come from Donegal when we was all drinkin' together last night . . .

Policeman. Drinkin'!

Mrs. Gray. Mrs. Docherty her name was, I've told you twenty times . . .

(Gray, with hesitant, frightened fingers touches his own mouth.)

Gray. And now there's blood all over here . . .

Policeman *(Placatingly).* Just take it easy, now. I'll come with you, by and by . . .

Mrs. Gray *(Dully, as though repeating a lesson).* Mrs. Docherty her name was . . . They killed her . . . Burke and Hare . . .

Policeman *(Undecided what to do).* Well, now . . .

Mrs. Gray. She followed me, she did, out of the house . . .

Policeman *(Puzzled).* Followed you?

Mrs. Gray. Mrs. Hare did. She said there'd never be a week after this, but that we'd be worth ten pounds more at the end of it . . .

Gray. I said my conscience would not allow me to do it.

Policeman *(Trying to catch up).* You say she followed you?

Mrs. Gray. Ay. She followed us into the street and she inquired what we were making a noise about, and she said 'Can't we go into the house and decide our matters there and not make a noise about them here?'

Gray. And I said my conscience would not allow me to do it, I say.

Shouts of. Where are they? Where are they?

Singing. Up the alley and down the street
      Dan is strong and Jennie's sweet
    Jennie's the maid who milks the cow,
    And Dan's the man who shows her how.

Policeman. We'll go and have a word with these people you've been telling me of. There may be something here that's worth a little looking into.

(The **Crowd,** *glad of this excitement, dance and sing in great glee as the* **Policeman** *is led by* **Gray** *and* **Mrs. Gray** *towards* **Log's Lodging House.***)*

(Burke, Hare, Mrs. Hare and Helen M'Dougal are in the room. The noise of the crowd singing and shouting outside the lodging house gives the impression that the place is under siege. Behind the Policeman, standing close together for protection, are Gray and Mrs. Gray.)

Hare. This is my house. I'll be wanting to know what you're doing in it.

Policeman. I'll be wanting a word or two with you, that's all . . .

(The more forward Members of the Crowd creep into the room so that they can see and hear better.)

Hare. Ye'd better be quick. We've work to do.

Policeman. These two people tell me they've seen a body in this room this morning.

Burke. There's no body here. Only the four live bodies you see before you. And a few extra ones we could well do without.

Mrs. Gray. There may not be a body here now. There was, when I was here before.

Burke. The woman's a fool. She's mad.

Policeman. Then you'll tell me, perhaps, what has become of your lodgers?

Hare *(Pointing to Gray)*. That's one of them. I turned him out of the house, and his wife, for their bad conduct. They was boxin', an' that, so that there wasn't ever any peace for civilized folks like the rest of us.

Mrs. Gray *(To the Policeman)*. Ask him what has happened to the little woman that was here yesterday.

Policeman *(To Hare)*. You heard her. What has happened to the little woman that was here yesterday?

Hare. She's away.

Policeman. When did she leave the house?

Hare. About seven o'clock in the morning.

Policeman. Did anyone but you see her go?

Hare. Yes. Burke here saw her go.

Mrs. Hare. She was so fashous I told her to go with the toe of my boot.

Policeman. Did any other person see her go away?

Hare *(Insolently).* Oh, yes, there were a number more.

Burke. And where did the old fools tell ye they saw the body, Sir? . . .

(Mrs. Gray points to the pile of cloths and straw. The Policeman kicks some of the straw aside. Hare laughs.)

. . . Maybe the mice, they dragged it down their little hole.

(The Policeman bends down to stare at the floorboards.)

Policeman. Blood on the boards.

(There is a moment's silence.)

Burke. And has there ever been, for the love o' God, a Hallowe'en party with no blood spilt? We was all convivial; there was fightin' in every room in the house.

Mrs. Hare. And as for the old woman you're so worried about, I can find her for you any time you want her. I know her perfectly well. She lives in the Pleasance. I've seen her this very morning, in the Vennel, and she apologized to me for her bad conduct last night.

Policeman. What time do you say she left the house?

Mrs. Hare. Why, about seven o'clock last night, wasn't it? We was having that merry an old time, I don't remember exactly.

Helen M'Dougal *(Pointing to the Grays).* And its they were picking the pockets of the poor innocent persons that couldn't get up from the floor . . .

Mrs. Hare. It's all lies, lies they were tellin' . . .

(The Policeman picks up the dress that Mrs. Gray had found.)

Helen M'Dougal. Don't you trust them, they're beggars, Sir . . .

Hare. They eat dead cats . . .

Mrs. Gray. That's Mrs. Docherty's dress . . . I mind the colour . . .

Hare. Fur and all . . .

Mrs. Hare. That's not hers, it's mine . . .

Policeman. There's blood on the front . . .

Mrs. Hare. Hare hit me with a glass in the face and the cut ran . . .

Gray. The old woman's face was a' slimy . . .

(The Policeman's slow mind registers the fact that the stories

47

told by **Hare** *and by* **Mrs. Hare** *are different. He stoops down, and ferrets around for a moment in the pile of clothes and straw. When he straightens himself, he has in his hand* **Ludovici's** *little wire cage—the cage we saw in the very first scene of this play. The white mice, in the cage, are dead.)*

Policeman. What's this?

(There is a sharp hiss, as at least three people in the group of silent onlookers recognise the cage.)

One Onlooker. That's Ludovici's . . .

A Second Onlooker. The devils . . .

A Third Onlooker. They've killed the little Italian boy . . .

The First Onlooker. The devils . . .

The Second Onlooker. They've killed the little Italian boy . . .

(The libel is bandied backwards and forwards between the onlookers in the room. Then it is handed outwards, to the readily excitable crowd outside. Soon, the crowd has become a mob—a mob shouting for vengeance for poor little Ludovici).

Voices. The devils . . .
They've killed the little Italian boy . . .
The devils . . .
Hang them, Hang them, Hang them!

(The **Policeman,** *realising that affairs are moving outside his control, draws a whistle from his belt and blows it, shrilly.)*

Hang them! . . .
The devils! . . .
They've killed the little Italian boy! . . .

Singing. Up the alley and down the street
Burke and Hare sell bones and meat,
Burke's the butcher, Hare's the thief,
And Knox is the boy who buys the beef.

Uproar. Hang them! Hang them! Where's little Ludovici? Etc. . .

(The **Policeman** *blows his whistle again. This time, there are answering whistles, and the crowd outside the lodging house cheers the* **Representatives of the Law** *as they appear. The* **Policeman** *makes signs towards* **Burke** *and* **Hare** *and they are quickly seized.)*

Policeman. Will you come quietly, the pair of you?

Burke. It's the truth I've been telling you, I say. It's the truth . . . May God strike me down dead, this minute, if I've told you one word of a lie!

(There is a shocked silence, for a moment, as everyone present waits for the Divine Judgment to be pronounced. Then the arrest of Burke *and* Hare, *and of* Mrs. Hare *and* Helen M'Dougal *takes place in an atmosphere of intense excitement.)*

9

THE ANATOMY THEATRE

(The Theatre fills, until it is crowded with students. Alexander Miller *is standing near* Doctor Knox.*)*

Doctor Knox *(Lecturing).* To destroy scabies, gentlemen, you do not wear the armour of defence, you wield the weapon of sulphur ointment. To think, then, is to enter into a perilous country, colder of welcome than the polar wastes, darker than a Scottish Sunday, where the hand of the unthinker is always raised against you, where the wild animals, who go by such names as Envy, Hypocrisy, and Tradition, are notoriously carnivorous, and *where the parasites rule.*

To *think* is dangerous. The majority of men have found it easier to writhe their way into the parasitical bureaucracy, or to *droop* into the slack ranks of the ruled. I beg you all to devote your lives to danger; I pledge you to adventure; I command you to experiment . . .

(He speaks slowly.)

. . . Remember that the practice of Anatomy is absolutely vital to the *progress* of medicine Remember that the progress of medicine is vital to the progress of mankind. And mankind is worth fighting for: killing and lying and dying for. Forget what you like. Forget all I have ever told you. But remember that . . .

*(*David Paterson *approaches.)*

David Paterson. The police have been here.

Doctor Knox. What is yours, Sir? A rum and bitters?

49

David Paterson *(Bewildered).* Sir?

Doctor Knox. Since you do not knock before you walk in, I must assume that this is a public-house . . .

David Paterson. I beg your pardon, Sir, but the police came about the new subject. Burke and Hare, Sir . . .

Doctor Knox. Am I never to hear the end of those men's names?

Alexander Miller *(Softly).* Never, perhaps . . .

David Paterson. And they're taking the subject away . . .

Doctor Knox. Why didn't you call the police? . . .

David Paterson *(More bewildered).* Sir, I . . .

Doctor Knox. Go away and lock up the silver. If there isn't any silver, lock up Mr. Miller here: he has a gold tooth.

(And **David Paterson** *goes out.)*

Alexander Miller. Must you antagonize every one?

Doctor Knox. Yes.

Alexander Miller. You heard? The police.

Doctor Knox. Outside the gates of hell are not the words 'Abandon Hope All Ye Who Enter Here', but 'I Told You So'.

Alexander Miller. And if the police ask me questions, as they are bound to do, what shall I say?

Doctor Knox. Say nothing. Squeak. They will recognize the voice of a rat . . .

(**Alexander Miller** *walks away in disgust. As he is about to disappear,* **Doctor Knox** *speaks again.)*

. . . You will find cheese in the larder. Leave some for David Paterson.

(If there were a door to slam, **Alexander Miller** *would slam it. The sardonicism and the mockery vanish from the face of* **Doctor Knox.**

Then, we hear the soft growing background of the crowd noise.

There is singing again:
'Up the alley and down the street . . . ' etc.
Then the noise of the crowd rises violently.
Through the noise of the crowd, we hear the percussive voice-beat of 'Knox! Knox! Knox!'
And, like a cymbal clashing, the sharp crash of smashed

50

*glass, as stones hurtle through the windows at one side of the
Anatomy Theatre.*

*The **students** stampede, as a heavy stone crashes at **Doctor
Knox**'s feet. They are shouting.*

Doctor Knox *stands rigid.*

*He pales with temper, glaring at the rushing students as
though they are his enemies.*

In its intensity, his dignity is malevolent.)

Doctor Knox. Gentlemen! . . .

*(His cold, controlled fury stops the rush. The **students** stand frozen.
The noise of the crowd can still be heard.)*

. . . I have attempted to teach you the dignity of man; I have
succeeded in producing the degradation of a *mob*. Because the
verminous gutter-snipes of the City snarl and gibber in the
street, because the scum from the brothels and the rot-gut shops
howl for blood outside my window, must *you* conduct yourselves,
in return, as though you were born in a quagmire and nurtured on
hog-wash?

Take your places again. Pay no attention to *the mob*. The
mob can never win. Remember that the louder a man shouts, the
emptier is his argument.

Remember that you are here to study osteology,
syndesmology, myology, angiology, neurology, splanchnology:
not bar-room pugilism or the morals of the crapulous bog-trotter
and the tosspot . . .

(He speaks in his usual lecturing voice.)

. . . The heart, gentlemen, is a four-chambered muscular bag which
lies in the cavity of the thorax . . .

The Crowd, on the fringes of The Anatomy Theatre:
  Knox! Knox! We want Knox!
  Knox! Knox! We want Knox!

Singing. Up the alley and down the street
  All our friends are Knox's meat;
  Burke's the butcher and Hare's the thief
  And Knox is the boy who buys the beef.

*(The **Crowd** seems to be wheeling round the **Anatomy Theatre**,
unable to disperse the tightly knit nucleus of **Students**.)*

Voices of the Crowd. Knox! Knox!
Hang Knox!
Burn him!
Burn!
Burn!
Knox is the boy who buys the beef . . .

(Suddenly, we see that someone in the crowd is carrying an effigy of **Doctor Knox**—*an absurdly top-hatted scarecrow. The other members of the crowd wave their fists and stamp and sing and howl, making a witches' Sabbath in the usually decorous* **Anatomy Theatre.**

And then the effigy, the guy carried on a pole, is held in a position directly opposite **Doctor Knox's** *lecturing table. The crowd salutes the effigy, crying in a high, hysterical triumph.*

Then, amid cries of 'Burn him! Burn Doctor Knox!' the effigy is carried out to the street; and the dark figures of the crowd follow, so that all can be present at the ceremonial burning of the scarecrow in the City Market Place.

The **Students** *follow, too, leaving* **Doctor Knox** *alone with* **Alexander Miller** *in the wrecked and littered* **Anatomy Theatre.**)

Alexander Miller. They say that Burke and Hare are being examined at the Police Office, Sir.

Doctor Knox. The better for them, I am sure.

Alexander Miller. They say that Hare has turned king's evidence, Sir.

Doctor Knox. The king will be pleased . . .

(From the distance, we hear the noise of the **Crowd. Doctor Knox** *talks on, as though to himself.)*

. . . I was successful, I was established, I was standing in the light . . . Then out of the mud of the darkness come two ignorant animals, and slowly, quite unknown to themselves, they set about the task of bringing my life and my work down, down, into the slime that bred them . . . Perhaps from the very moment of their monstrous births, it was decreed, by some sadistic jack-in-office of the universe, that they should befoul and ruin a fellow creature they had never heard of: a garrulous, over-credulous, conceited little anatomist, in a city they had never seen . . .

Alexander Miller. I am sorry, Sir.

52

Doctor Knox. I have no need of your sympathy. When I see a tear, I smell a crocodile.

Alexander Miller *(Roused, suddenly, beyond endurance).* For God's sake, can you do nothing but—stand still and gibe?

Doctor Knox. Would you have me death-dance and moan, like a Gaelic dipsomaniac at a distillery fire? Must tragedy go immediately to the feet and the tongue? Because I can observe my history *calmly* as it burns and topples around me, you emotional gluttons think yourselves cheated. 'Oh, he can't *feel* anything', you say. 'When we told him his life was over, he did not tear the relics of his hair or address the travelling moon in blank verse. He blew his nose and called for Burgundy'.

Alexander Miller *(Deliberately).* Burke, they say, will hang.

Doctor Knox. A quick end. If they wished his end to be longer and infinitely more painful, they should marry him to Doctor Munro's daughter.

Alexander Miller. Mrs. Hare and the woman M'Dougal will probably stand trial with Burke. Hare, if it is true that he has turned King's Evidence, will be free to murder again. And *you*?

Doctor Knox. I shall stay here.

I shall listen to the voices of the crowd outside my window, *inside my head*; it will not be long before they forget me; I shall never forget them.

I shall stay here. The whisperers of the slanderer and the backbiter will always be with me: mice behind the wall.

I shall stay here. I shall count my friends on the fingers of one hand, then on one finger, then on none . . .

(A distant cheer, from the **Crowd** *in the City Market Place.)*

. . . My lectures will be very well attended, at the beginning. I shall possess a sinister attraction to the young: dangerous and exciting, like dining with a vampire. But the attendance will diminish.

I shall stay here to see in the eyes of the passing stranger in the street cruelty and contempt; in the eyes of the poor the terrible accusation: 'You killed the lost, the weak, the homeless, the hopeless, the helpless. Murderer of the poor!'

God help me, life will go on . . .

*(***Doctor Knox** *turns and walks slowly away. As he does so, he almost stumbles over a* **Little Girl** *who is crouching in the shadows.*

She is grimed from the gutters of the city; her dress is thin, and ragged; one shoulder is naked.)

The Little Girl. Give us a penny, Mister. Give us a penny . . .

*(***Doctor Knox** *stops, looks down, and puts a penny in the* **Little Girl's** *hand.)*

Doctor Knox. You oughtn't to be here, lassie. You ought to be outside. But it's bitter cold weather to be running about in the streets. You should go home.

(The **Little Girl** *shakes her head.)*

The Little Girl. Granny says I can't go home till I get fourpence.

*(***Doctor Knox** *draws in his breath, sharply. Then he fumbles in his pocket for more coins. The* **Little Girl** *holds out her hand.)*

Doctor Knox. What's your name, child?

The Little Girl. I'm Maggie Bell.

Doctor Knox *(Almost as though to himself).* And I'm Doctor Knox . . .

(The **Little Girl** *throws down her penny, and runs away, screaming.)*

. . . And the child in the cold runs away from my name. My name is a ghost to frighten children.

Will my children cry 'Murder' and 'Blood' when I touch them, as if my hands were Burke's hands?

'Be good, be good, or the terrible Doctor will come with his knife'.

Singing *(Possibly, from a distance).* Poor Jamie ne'er was shrouded,
But in a tea-chest crowded,
With coffin ne'er connected,
But with the knife dissected . . .

Doctor Knox. Poor Jamie! I came to you with my knife.
Did I *know*, did I *know* from the very beginning?
Never answer, never answer, even to yourself alone in the night . . .
All's over now . . . All's over, for ever . . .
Did I set myself up as a little god over death?
Over death . . .
All over . . . over . . . over . . .
Did I set myself above pity?
Oh, my God, I knew what I was doing!

54